HAPPY BURGER

A PLAY BY
CHUCK RANBERG AND PATRICK DALEY

SCHOLASTIC INC.

New York   Toronto   London   Auckland   Sydney
Mexico City   New Delhi   Hong Kong

COVER ILLUSTRATION BY
GREG JOHANNES

INTERIOR ILLUSTRATIONS BY
PETER SPACEK

"Happy Burger" was first published in
Scholastic Action® magazine, Vol. 15, No. 4/5, November 1/15, 1991.

Text copyright © 1991 by Scholastic Inc.
Illustrations copyright © 1999 by Scholastic Inc.
All rights reserved. Published by Scholastic Inc.
Printed in the United States of America. 113

ISBN 0-439-05710-8

26 25 24 23   R   12 13 14 15

Scott learns that life is full of surprises—and they don't always involve a clown hat.

Narrator: I told Stacy I couldn't afford the dance. She could have said, "Don't worry, Scott, I'll pay for the tickets." She also could have said, "Let's just go to the movies or do something that's really cheap." She could have said a lot of things. Instead she dropped me faster than yesterday's french fries. But a few nights later, Carol called.

Carol *(on the phone)*: Hi, Scott. I heard you weren't going to your dance. And, I was wondering, if . . . well, if you'd like to go to the homecoming dance at my school with me.

Scott: Sure, Carol. I'll go with you. Um . . . you didn't ask Spike first, did you?

Carol: Please, Scott. I want to go out on a *date*—not a disaster!

Narrator: So, that's how I learned that life is full of surprises. And sometimes an experience that is a bummer can lead to something good. Or as Dad would say, this is how lemonade is made out of lemons. Carol and I had a great time at the dance. And guess where we went afterwards? You got it. Happy Burger. We've been together ever since.

Is the ending anything like what you expected? What do you think Scott has learned about Stacy? What do you think he's learned about Mr. Hennings?

CHARACTERS

Narrator - Scott Wheeler today

Scott Wheeler - several years ago

Mr. Wheeler - his father

Mr. Hennings - the manager of Happy Burger

Carol - a worker at Happy Burger

Spike - a worker at Happy Burger

Stacy - Scott's dream girl

Customer #1

Customer #2

Scott is ready for his date. All he needs is money—BIG money.

Narrator: Dad was funny. You couldn't just come right out and ask him for money. You had to sneak it into the conversation. That night at dinner, I was ready for my sneak attack.

Scott: Dad, I have some good news and some bad news. The good news is . . .

Mr. Wheeler *(interrupting)*: How much money do you need, Scott?

Narrator: Dad was also smart. I needed to try a new angle.

Scott: Dad, a totally amazing thing happened today. The girl of my dreams said she'd go to the homecoming dance with me. Isn't that unbelievable?

Mr. Wheeler: Amazing. So how much money do you need?

Narrator: I forgot to mention that Dad definitely wasn't very romantic.

Scott: Seriously, Dad, her name is Stacy. She's the most beautiful girl in school. All I need is enough money to buy tickets, rent a tux, and take her to dinner. How does that sound?

Mr. Wheeler: Sounds great, Scott. I'd be glad to help you out with your dream date.

Scott: You would?

Mr. Wheeler: Sure. Bring me the newspaper.

Scott: The paper? What for?

Mr. Wheeler: So I can help you look for a job.

The great job hunt finally ends. And Scott's wearing a clown hat.

Narrator: Job hunting was a drag. My choices quickly came down to fast food or shampooing dogs at the local pet store. I'm not big on washing anything that can bite, so I chose a place called Happy Burger.

Mr. Hennings: Welcome to the Happy Burger family, Scotty-boy. You're going to love it here!

Narrator: My new boss was one of those people who *really* loves his job. And I'm one of those people who *hates* to be called Scotty-boy.

Scott: Thanks. I'll see you tomorrow after school.

Mr. Hennings: Good. By the way, what size clown hat do you wear?

Narrator: Oh yeah, that was the other thing. All Happy Burger employees wear clown hats. I just kept reminding myself that this clown hat was going to pay for my big date.

Scott joins the Happy Burger family, and he makes close friends—with the Fry-O-Matic.

Narrator: Soon, it was my first day on the job.

Mr. Hennings: This is the Fry-O-Matic, Scotty-boy. It makes up to four thousand french fries an hour. Get to know it. Make it your friend.

Scott: Nice to meet you, Fry-O-Matic.

Mr. Hennings: That's clever, Scotty-boy. Now if you have any questions, just ask Carol. She's a good Happy Burger employee. (*whispering*) You might not want to ask Spike too many questions. He doesn't know where his head stops and the clown hat begins!

Narrator: Carol and Spike were part of my Happy Burger family. Carol was a junior at another high school. She was friendly and had a nice smile. Spike was in college—or so he said. But I never saw him studying. In fact, it wasn't very often that I even saw him working!

Scott is making his Dad so proud. . . .

Narrator: A few days later, Dad and I were talking about my new career.

Mr. Wheeler: So, how's work going these days?

Scott: Pretty good, Dad. I've mastered french fries. I'm a pro at triple-thick shakes. And I can finally put those plastic lids on sodas without making a huge mess.

Mr. Wheeler: Congratulations, Scott. You'll always be able to use those kinds of skills in real life. Hey, do I smell french fries cooking in the kitchen?

Scott: Um, no. That must be me. The smell kind of stays with you. I guess I'll go take a shower.

Mr. Wheeler: Good idea.

Repeat after me: Polite, money, food. Polite, money, food. . . .

Narrator: A week later, I was moved up to the front lines. The field of battle. Yes, I was ready for the customer service register!

Spike *(to Carol)*: How come Scott's on the register already? I've been here longer, and I'm still making fries!

Carol: Mr. Hennings is probably afraid you'll scare the customers . . . again.

Spike: It's not fair. I haven't scared hardly anybody in weeks!

Carol *(to Scott)*: Don't worry. All you have to remember is to be polite—that's the Happy Burger policy. And get the money before you give them the food.

Scott *(nervously)*: Right, the Happy Burger motto: Polite, money, food. Polite, money, food. Okay, I think I've got it now.

Carol: Trust me, Scott. You'll do fine. Don't worry.

Spike: Get ready, boys and girls. Here come the hungry cattle!

Narrator: Every day the food stampede started at about five o'clock. People rushed in right after work to buy Happy Burgers to take home to their happy families.

Customer #1 *(speaking fast)*: Give me two Happy Doubles. One Happy Original with cheese. A Happy-But-Lean . . .

Narrator: Little beads of sweat were starting to form on my forehead. My shirt collar started to feel really tight.

Customer #1 *(continuing)*: A Baby Happy and a small order of fries. And a chocolate shake, a large iced tea, and a small diet soda *(pause)* with lemon on the side.

Scott: Yes, sir, right away. *(pause)* Um, could you repeat that for me please?

Is there disaster at the end of the line?

Narrator: Somehow, I got through that first rush hour. And some days I actually had fun. Carol was really nice and kind of cute, too. Spike was pretty funny, and he was becoming a good buddy. But then one day, something happened that I hadn't ever expected.

Spike: Hey, Scott, check out the babe at the end of your line. I think I'm in serious love!

Narrator: I followed Spike's gaze down the line. All of a sudden—yikes! My stomach did a back flip. It was Stacy. You see, I hadn't exactly told her the truth about my new job. *Somehow* she got the impression that I worked at a *fancy* restaurant.

Scott: Uh, Carol, could you handle things up here for a few minutes? I feel kind of sick.

Carol: Oh, that's just the fumes from the kitchen. You'll get used to it.

Scott: No, I really think I need a break. *Please?*

Carol: Well, all right. Hurry back, okay? It's more fun when you're here.

Scott: Thanks. You're a lifesaver!

Stacy: Scott? What are *you* doing here?

Narrator: Busted! Stacy saw me. I had no choice but to be cool. Yes, that was it—be cool and bluff my way out.

Scott: Oh hi, Stacy. What can I get you? The fries are especially crisp tonight.

Stacy: What's going on? Is this a joke? I thought you were working in a restaurant.

Scott *(in a French accent)*: But madame, isn't this a restaurant?

Stacy: You know what I mean, Scott. Someplace nice—not a creepy hamburger place.

Scott: Okay, I guess I should have told you. But it doesn't matter, does it? I'll take you someplace really nice—and expensive—after the dance.

Stacy: I hope so!

Scott: I swear—cross my heart!

Stacy: Okay. Now could I have a large diet cola?

Scott: Sure, Stacy. I'll get you anything you want.

Carol: *I'll* get it for you, Scott.

Narrator: Behind my lovesick back, Carol filled a big cup with our sweetest, non-diet cola.

Carol *(faking being nice)*: Here you go, miss!

Scott: Thanks. Anything else, Stacy?

Stacy: Just one thing. Before we go out, lose the clown hat, okay?

Scott *(embarrassed)*: Oh yeah, sure!

Narrator: With that, Stacy walked out. I wondered how many extra hours I'd have to work to pay for the fancy dinner I'd just promised her. I got the answer the next day. But it wasn't the answer I expected.

Will Scott work the extra hours to pay for the date with Stacy? How will the date go? Make some predictions.

Customers are always right—except when they're wrong.

Narrator: Carol and I were jammin' at the front counter. It was a really rainy day. Most of the people in line were soggier than the lettuce that tops our burgers. Suddenly, an angry customer came up to Carol.

Customer #2: Hey lady, this is the worst hamburger I've ever tasted in my entire life. I want my money back!

Narrator: Carol remembered the Happy Burger motto, "polite, money, food." She tried to talk politely to the customer.

Carol: I'm sorry about that, sir. Why don't I just give you another hamburger?

Customer #2: I don't want another lousy burger! Just my money!

Narrator: Carol was starting to get nervous. I was getting nervous for her, too.

Carol: I'm sorry, sir, but I can't give you a refund.

Customer #2: Read my lips, you fool! I want my money back. And I want it now!

Narrator: That was it! I wasn't going to stand around and let this guy insult my friend. After all, Carol worked hard and she was a great kid.

Scott: Hey mister, there's no need to talk to her like that. It's not her fault.

Customer #2: Listen, clown, it's not my fault you're all idiots. Now do I get my money back, or do I call the manager?

Scott *(angry)*: Why don't you take your Happy Burger and choke on it, bubble-head?

Narrator: Okay, I know. I may have gotten a little carried away. But I knew Mr. Hennings would stick up for me. After all, Mr. Hennings would be loyal to his Happy Burger family. He would understand.

Mr. Hennings: I'm sorry, Scott. I know you meant well. But we can't have unhappy customers here at Happy Burger. It's time to turn in your hat. You're fired.

Narrator: Fired? That's just great! My first job, and I get fired.

Scott's career at Happy Burger left him with more than just a few grease stains on his clothes.

ACT 8

Narrator: And so my burger career ended. That night I broke the news to Dad.

Dad: Well, Scott, there's always a lesson to be learned from an experience like this.

Narrator: Good old Dad! He was pretty big on life lessons.

Dad: When life gives you lemons, you . . .

Scott: Yeah, I know. You make lemonade.

Narrator: I had heard this lesson before.

Dad: Exactly! Now I am sure this will all work out for the best.

Scott: Maybe you're right, Dad. I guess I'll tell Stacy that my finances just took a bad turn.